WELSH AND SCOTTISH
POSTBUS TICKETS
1967 – 1999

ERIC C. MOLES

The Transport Ticket Society
2001

Cover photograph:
A Landrover Postbus in the remote area of Kinlochourn.
[courtesy Ken Ross]

Comments etc. regarding this publication are welcome;
please write to the Society's Publications Officer:

David Harman
24 Frankfield Rise
Tunbridge Wells
TN2 5LF

E-Mail: David.Harman@btinternet.com

© Copyright Eric C. Moles, 2001

ISBN 0 903209 53 5

Published by
The Transport Ticket Society
81 Pilgrims Way, Kemsing, Sevenoaks, TN15 6TD

Printed by
Paterson Printing Ltd,
Tunbridge Wells

Preface

This publication looks at the Postbus tickets of Wales and Scotland from the inception of Postbus services in 1967 and 1968 respectively.

Many people from the Royal Mail have assisted me in producing this publication. In particular I would like to thank:

Ken Ross - Postbus Manager, Inverness.
Ann Simpson - Postbus Manager, Plymouth (now retired)
Tony Wickham - Postbus Administration, Bath

Also a special thank-you to my wife, Doreen, who typed the original draft, and without whose help this publication would not have materialised.

Eric C Moles
Settle, North Yorkshire
January 2001

Index

The decline of the local independent bus operators and the reduction of market day services, it prompted the Wales & Marches Postal Board to commence the very first experimental Postbus service.

The service commenced on the 20th February 1967 between Llanidloes and Llangurig. This service has been a success as it is still in operation today.

The English and Scottish Post Offices watched the situation carefully before commencing similar experimental services in 1967 and 1968 respectfully.

It was over ten years before the next Postbus service made its appearance in Wales, except for a special service in May 1972. From then on it was a slow expansion with only twenty-two further services being introduced. Some of these have since ceased operation.

Much has already been said about the Post Office becoming a Corporation. Like their counterparts in England and Scotland, the Welsh Post Office could apply for full rebates and subsidies towards operating costs.

In 1992 the Post Office structure was reorganised converting the Regions and the Wales & the Marches Board into Divisions. The services in mid and north Wales passed to the newly formed North Wales & North West Division, with South Wales services passing to South Wales & South West Division. These Divisions remained until the year 2000, when five Territories were formed.

On the first service, ticket machines were used for the first twelve years, but card tickets were in use on the second Postbus from 1977. With the commencement of Postbus services this gave the various collectors a choice of material to collect - i.e. Postbus fleet list, post cards, first day covers, special handstamps and tickets.

A T.I.M. machine No. 1 was introduced on the first Postbus service between Llanidloes and Llangurig on 20 February 1967 Issuing tickets titled 'POST OFFICE'.

This machine remained in service until 15 February 1971. The following day it was replaced by an Almex 'A' 0004 issuing 'POST OFFICE' titled tickets. This machine, like its predecessor gave good service, being withdrawn on 25 February 1979.

On 26 February 1979 horizontal printed white card tickets made their appearance. The title was bilingual - 'BWS Y POST BRENHINOL ROYAL MAIL BUS' printed in red with red crossed post horns on the left. There were three spaces for stamps, although on odd occasions four stamps have been used for the appropriate fare, then cancelled by a handstamp.

The cancellation handstamp had six lines of print - three lines in Welsh, and three lines in English. The date shown was the first day that this type of ticket came into use on the service. The following day an undated three-line cancellation handstamp with bilingual title came into regular use.

A commemorative postal minibus service was operated for the 54th Philatelic Congress of Great Britain for four days between 23 - 26 May 1972 from Llandudno to Colwyn Bay. A special ticket was produced, printed in red on white card. The ticket was headed with a crown with 'Llandudno' across the centre, 'Single fare Paid 10p' on lower half with 'POST OFFICE' above conditions at the foot.

Returning to the Postbus services - the next service commenced on 18 July 1977 between Llandovery and Myddfai. This was the first service to introduce the horizontally printed card. On the first day of the service a seven-line cancellation handstamp was used, showing in the text 'FIRST JOURNEY', presumably meaning first journey am and first journey pm.

The next day a handstamp with two-line bilingual title was used to cancel stamped cards. Soon after a three-line handstamp appeared, replacing the handstamp previously used. This new handstamp had the route details added.

18 July 1978 - the first anniversary of this service: It was suggested that a special eight-line cancellation handstamp was used. No ticket has been seen bearing this, so it cannot be confirmed.

During 1980 a new cancellation handstamp appeared, replacing the existing handstamp. The difference on the new handstamp was that the route was now shown in two lines.

From July 1977 to July 1986 services that were introduced during this period adopted the horizontally printed card as standard ticket issue. Each service produced a first journey handstamp, then on the following day a three-line version became the normal everyday cancellation handstamp. There were one or two exceptions to this - e.g. on the Llandrindod Wells - Llaithddu service, the second day handstamp was in four lines. During the late 1980's on the Llandrindod Wells - Rhayader service a two-line handstamp came into use.

From the very first horizontally printed card the bilingual title had always been in sans-serif capitals. In the mid 1980's on the Machynlleth - Aberhosan service an issue appeared with bilingual title in serif capitals.

In 1989 Almex 'A' machines began to replace the horizontal cards, and were titled 'Royal Mail Letters Postbus service'.

Known machines

Llanidloes - Llangurig	7581
Llandrindod Wells - Llaithddu	6527
Newtown - New Mills	7583
Builth Wells - Abergvesyn	75'??
Machynlleth - Aberhosan	6568
Llandrindod Wells - Rhayader	7669
Llanidloes - Dylife	7374
Builth Wells - Painscastle	unknown
Aberystwyth - Blaenpennal	6711
Aberystwyth - Cwmystwyth	7614 - 7581
Usk - Llandenny	6748
Abergavenny - Skenfrith	7346

An untitled Almex 'A' 8047 was also noted on the Machynlleth service.

The Welshpool - Foel service commenced 26 August 1993 using untitled Carbonised pad tickets by Transport Ticket Services. This was the first tine that this type of ticket had been used on any Welsh service.

Eventually, the pad tickets were replaced later in 1993 by an Almex 'A' machine - number unknown.

Two services from Pembroke Dock, and two services from Narberth commenced October 1994. These services were introduced by the new South Wales & South West Division. A new style of ticket was introduced. The new issue of tickets were duplex type printed in red on soft yellow card by a local printer. These were bilingual titled with 'S/WALES/S/WEST' in Welsh and English over "Postbus" in a centre box. Values start at 5p with increments of 5p to 95p and £1 - £2 - £3 - £4 - £5 with A-C-CON-M in boxes.

Special guests were invited on the inaugural journey, and they were issued with a duplex ticket overprinted with a black star. On the following journey, normal duplex tickets were issued.

During 1997 it was discovered that the tickets had changed colour to pale yellow with red text in thinner type. Values were as previously but there was a slight change in design: bilingual title in right-hand box, larger 'Postbus' in left-hand box, with 'S/WALES & S/WEST DIVISION' in the centre. Printed by a local printer.

Concessions
It is not known whether Royal Mail Wales ever issued their own concessionary tickets.

As the county councils and local councils commenced issuing concessionary tickets to senior citizens, blind persons, aid disabled, these gradually became valid on Postbuses.

Rovers, Explorers and Freedom Tickets
These types of tickets are not accepted on Postbuses.

Commenced	Route	Ceased
20 Feb 1967	Llanidloes - Llangurig	
23 May 1972	Llandudno - Colwyn Bay	26 May 1972
18 Jul 1977	Llandovery - Myddfai	
31Oct 1977	Rhyl - Meriadog	3 Aug 1984
26 Jun 1978	Llandrindod Wells - Llaithddu	
10 Jul 1978	Usk - Bettws Newydd	7 Aug 1981
10 Jul 1978	Usk - Llandenny	2 Sep 1991
4 Jun1979	Newtown - New Mills	
12 Nov 1979	Builth Wells - Abergwesyn	
19 Nov 1979	Machynlleth - Aberhosan	
7 Jan 1980	Aberystwyth - Blaenpennal	
23 Feb 1980	Abergavenny - Skenfrith	
19 May 1980	Llandrindod Wells - Rhayader	
8 Sep 1980	Llanidloes - Dylife	
17 Nov 1981	Rhayader - Abergwngu	18 Feb 1984
4 Jun 1984	Builth Wells - Painscastle	
1 Jul 1986	Aberystwyth - Cwmystwyth	
26 Aug 1993	Welshpool - Foel	
5 Sep 1994	Aberystwyth - Cwmerfyn	
3 Oct 1994	Pembroke Dock - Bosherston	1 Jul 2000
3 Oct 1994	Pembroke Dock - Angle	1 Jul 2000
31 Oct 1994	Narberth - Lawrenny	1 Jul 2000
31 Oct 1994	Narberth - Landshipping	1 Jul 2000
28 Apr 1997	Brecon - Talgarth	

Llanidloes - Llangurig

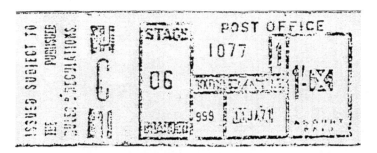

20 Feb 1967 to 15 Feb 1971

16 Feb 1971 to 25 Feb 1979

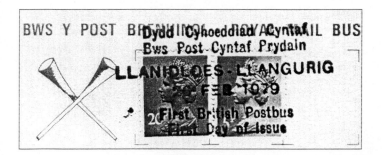

26 Feb 1979

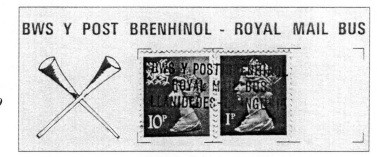

27 Feb 1979 to 1989

Llandudno - Colwyn Bay

23 - 26 May 1972

Llandovery - Myddfai

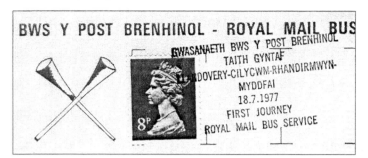

18 Jul 1977

19 Jul 1977

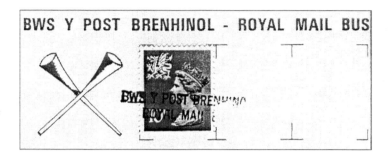

1980 to 1989

Rhyl - Meriadog

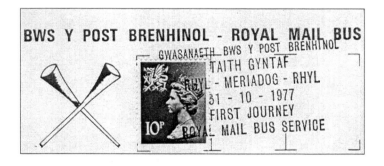

31 Oct 1977

1 Nov 1977 to 3 Aug 1984

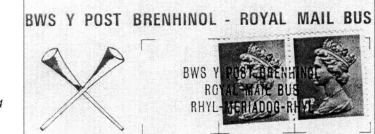

Llandrindod Wells - Llaithddu

26 Jun 1978

Usk - Llandenny

10 Jul 1978 to 1989

Newtown - New Mills

4 Jun 1979

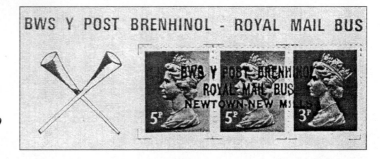

5 Jun 1979 to 1989

Builth Wells - Abergwesyn

12 Nov 1979

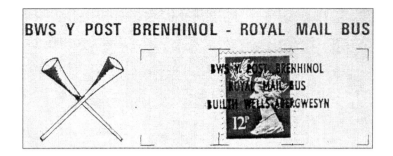

13 Nov 1979 to 1989

13 Nov 1979 to 1989

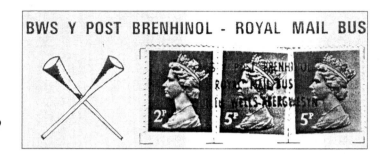

Machynlleth - Aberhosan

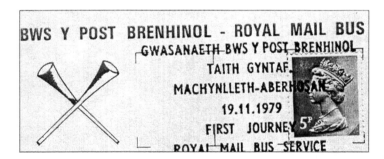

19 Nov 1979

20 Nov 1979

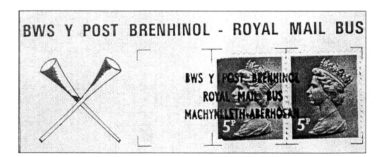

Mid 1980s to 1989

Aberystwyth - Blaenpennal

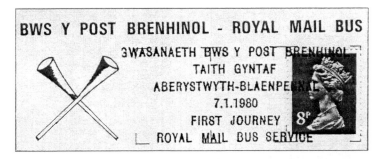

7 Jan 1980

8 Jan 1980 to 1989

Aberystwyth - Skenfrith

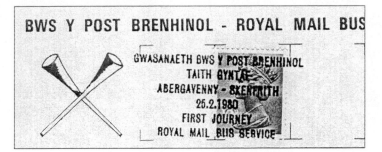

25 Feb 1980

26 Feb 1980 to 1989

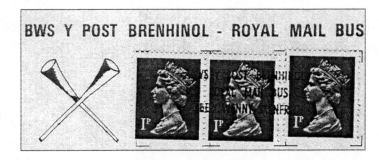

Llandrindod Wells - Rhayader

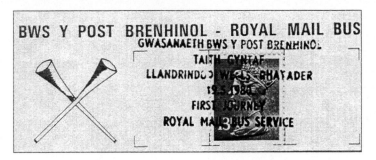

19 May 1980

20 May 1980

Mid 1980s to 1989

Llanidloes - Dylife

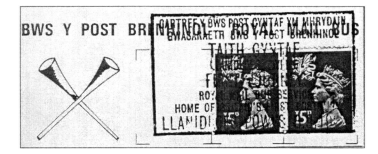

8 Sep 1980

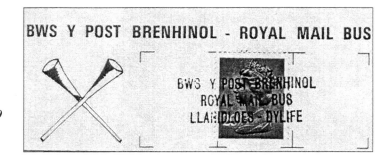

8 Jan 1980 to 1989

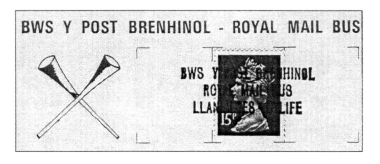

1980 to 1989

Rhayader - Abergwngu

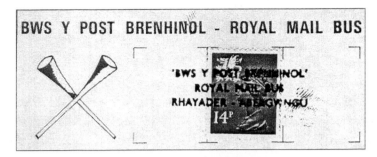

17 Nov 1981 to 18 Feb 1984

North Wales Services

from 1989

Welshpool - Foel

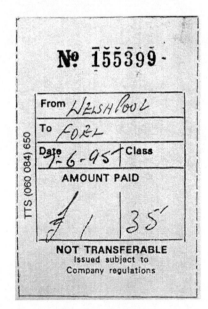

26 Aug 1993

South Wales Services

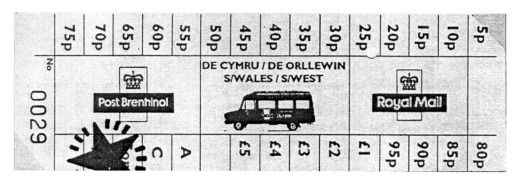

Oct 1994

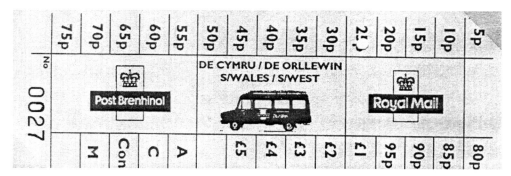

Oct 1994

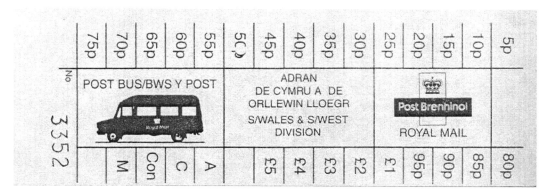

From approximately 1997

Transporting of the mails to the remote parts of Scotland and its islands has always been a complex business. The Scottish Post Office found it a very costly operation, and the attention turned to the independent bus operator, offering him a contract to carry the Royal Mail for a reasonable return.

The bus operator who accepted these contracts had to conform to strict regulations laid down by the Post Office. For example the vehicles had to be adapted to carry the mail in compartment separated from the travelling public. The compartment also had to be securely locked.

These arrangements continued for many years until the 1950s when passenger loadings started to fall, and the operators began to reduce their services, eventually withdrawing them altogether.

This situation must have put great pressure on the Post Office to find an alternative solution, not only to deliver mail but to collect mail from airports and sea ports.

The Scottish Post Office decided to follow England and Wales, to put on an experimental Postbus service, and on 4 June 1968 the Postbus made its inaugural journey between Dunbar and Innerwick.

In 1969 the Post Office ceased to be a government department, and became a nationalised business. This made a large difference to the Scottish Post Office, enabling them to apply for fuel rebates, grants towards new vehicles, and subsidies towards running costs.

The Dunbar experimental Postbus service was successful, but it was nearly four years later before further services commenced in 1972. The Postal Board consulted local authorities, development boards, and local communities becoming aware of local needs, carrying on by tradition the services that had been offered by the previous bus operator.

The function of the Scottish Postbus is similar to their counterparts in England and Wales, the only difference being that most of the services operate in very rural areas.

By the end of 1972 ten services were in operation. Rapid development and expansion continued through the 1970's and 1980's with steady growth continuing through to today.

Ticket machines played a prominent part in the early years of development of the Postbus services. The first to be adopted was a secondhand T.I.M.

When new services were introduced, the ticket system improved bringing into operation Almex 'A', Setright Speed and printed roll tickets. At first it was not difficult to follow the progress of ticket machines in use, but as new services were being developed, with further ticket machines being introduced, it became difficult to follow all developments, particularly when other machines replaced equipment that had broken down or was being serviced.

In 1973 concessionary tickets made their first appearance, followed in 1974 by the first roll tickets, these being untitled. Titled issues did not materialise until 1976.

In 1986 reorganisation of the Post Office took place forming three separate businesses: Post Office Counters Ltd, Parcelforce and Royal Mail Letters. Since 1934 the Post Office was divided into nine Regions, these remaining in force until 1992 when they were formed into Divisions with modified boundaries, but in each case no change to Scotland. In the year 2000 the Divisions have disbanded in favour of five Territories.

For the collector or specialist there is still a wealth of material available - photographs; post cards; first day covers, and first day special hand stamps, together with of course - tickets.

The Kinlochourn Postbus in rugged country
[Photograph, courtesy Ken Ross]

1 The first machine to be put into service in June 1968 was an ex-Bolton Corporation T.I.M. B109. The Post Office modified the printing plate to issue "Post Office" titled tickets. The T.I.M. remained in service until late 1969 when it began to develop mechanical problems, and the machine was withdrawn. At that time there was no suitable machine available as a replacement, so there was a period when tickets were not issued.

2 On the 15 February 1971 the monetary system changed from £.s.d. to decimal currency. At this time the Scottish Post Office introduced an Almex 'A' machine 0002 issuing tickets titled 'POST OFFICE'. This was the first Almex 'A' the Scottish Post Office had put into operation.

It appears to have given a good account of itself as the machine was not withdrawn until 1974.

The second Postbus service commenced 27 April 1972 on the Isle of Skye, between Elgol and Broadford. From the start Almex 'A' 0001 was put to work issuing tickets titled 'POST OFFICE'. The machine was originally used in Devon on the Honiton to Luppit service, but this machine did not last long at Elgol, and was replaced by an untitled Almex 'A', presumed to be ex-David Macbrayne Ltd.

3 During the next eight months a further eight services had commenced. It was during this period that Setright Speeds made their appearance.

The Scottish Postal Board had purchased these machines from Maidstone & District Motor Services Ltd. during 1972. The machines were easily identifiable as they had 'Z' prefix to the machine number. None of the machines were adapted to print a title, nor any titled rolls printed. Therefore, 'TRANSPORT SERVICE' rolls by GNP. Co. Ltd. were used at first. Later, plain rolls were adopted.

There was also one further Setright Speed machine in use. This was 2390, which is believed to have been obtained from Edinburgh Corporation.

4 Lockerbie - St. Anns service commenced in 1973. It has been suggested that a titled card ticket was used from its inception by the Scottish Postal Board commemorating five years of Postbus operation in Scotland. There has not been any confirmation of this ticket, so we must keep an open mind.

5 Later in 1973, September to be precise, the Postal Board produced a 2" square soft card ticket for the Thornhill-Moniave service. The ticket, light orange in colour had a crown above "Post Office" between two lines followed by route details. On the reverse, there was space for the fare to be handwritten with serial number at the foot.

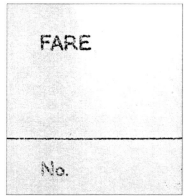

6 On 1 October 1973 the Scottish Postal Board acquired the stage service on the Isle of Islay, which was previously operated by Highland Omnibuses Ltd. This was a landmark in Scottish Postal Board Postbus operations as this became the 25th service. To commemorate this achievement a thin card was produced to which stamps were affixed to the fare for the journey. This was cancelled by a specially designed handstamp. This was the first time cards had been used with stamps affixed.

7 By November, additional tickets had appeared. This was a Concessionary ticket, produced by the Post Office. Salmon in colour with the crown over "Post Office", between two lines with "Islay Postbus

Services" on the lower half. On the reverse the ticket is headed "Concessionary Fare" with a bold "5p" in the centre with the ticket number at the foot.

These tickets were passed to the Islay District Council for distribution to their senior citizens.

9 On 1 April 1974 the Post Office issued a new style of Concessionary ticket for the Isle of Islay Postbus service. This was valid to 30 September 1974. On the front it had the crown over "Post Office", with "Islay Postbus Service Concessionary Ticket" beneath. There was a space for the name and address of the holder.

On the reverse there were fifty cancellation boxes, each containing '5p' and a box number, each being cancelled when produced to the driver. The ticket was on salmon card with black text.

8 On 3 January 1974 services at Aberfeldy started. At the commencement of these services, a new ticket system was introduced: roll tickets by G.N.P. These were untitled and without imprint. This was the first tine that preprinted tickets had been used for general service.

10 A further variation of roll ticket appeared later in 1974, still untitled, but now with G.N.P. Co. LTD. imprint.

Known values:-

2p	buff	5p	yellow
2p	white	5p	brown
2p	blue	5p	lilac
2p	red	10p	pink
3p	green	10p	lilac
3p	lilac	10p	brown
3p	buff	10p	buff;
3p	orange	10p	violet
3p	blue	10p	grey
3p	brown	10p	blue
3p	grey	10p	orange
3p	yellow	10p	green
3p	white	20p	blue
5p	grey	20p	violet
5p	green	20p	buff
5p	orange	20p	grey
5p	pink	20p	orange
5p	blue	20p	red
5p	white	20p	lilac
5p	violet	20p	green
5p	buff	50p	orange

Known values:-

2p	lilac	2p	puce
2p	orange	2p	yellow
2p	blue	3p	pink
2p	green	3p	orange
2p	pink	3p	green
2p	magenta		

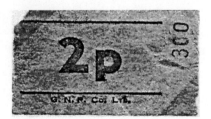

11 T.I.M. B109 reappeared in August 1974, this time on the West Calder-Tarbrax service, three-and-a-half years after its withdrawal for repairs. The fate of this machine is not known.

12 Returning to the Isle of Islay, the Post Office

introduced a further Concessionary ticket. This was similar in design to the previous issue, available from 1 October 1974 until 31 March 1975. On this occasion it was red with black text.

13 Dingwall - Heights of Docherty Postbus service commenced in March 1975. This was the one hundredth service. To honour this milestone the Post Office issued a card to take affixed stamps, cancelling them with a specially designed handstamp.

14 Printed roll tickets began to appear on many routes, but Aberfoyle Delivery Office went one step further, by cancelling them with a 1" diameter handstamp. The cancellation handstamp had the date in the centre with 'ABERFOYLE, STIRLING' round the inside edge.

Three values known:-

5p	green	10p	grey
5p	orange		

They were untitled and without imprint. It is possible there were other values, which were similarly treated.

15 The first titled roll tickets appeared possibly early 1976. They were titled "SCOTTISH POSTBUS SERVICES" in plain capitals with an imprint of G.N.P. Co. Ltd. The value in bold type as previous. It will be noted that the 'O's' in "Scottish" and Postbus" were of oval type.

Known values :-

2p	pale pink	20p	dark orange
3p	blue	50p	deep pink
5p	green	50p	lilac
10p	buff	Concession	white

15a The tickets in this issue are identical in style to the previous issue except that the 'O's' in "Scottish" and "Postbus" are round.

Known values

3p	blue	20p	burnt orange
10p	stone	25p	pink

From this period, ticket issue stabilised as most services introduced adopted the pre-printed roll tickets. There were occasional services that used a Setright Speed machine.

As the roll tickets continued to make their appearance, the dates shown are approximate, because in most cases new prints replaced old stock. It made it difficult to keep up to date with all the changes, also due to new values being required for fare increases.

16 It was during 1982 the next phase of roll tickets appeared. Although the style of title and design of tickets were the same as issue (15),the only difference being that the imprint now showed 'G.N.P. - BOOTH LTD.'

Known values:-

2p	pink	50p	slate
3p	blue	50p	lilac
5p	green	£1.00	light green
5p	turquoise	£2.00	brown
10p	buff	Concession	white
20p	brick-shades to orange		

16a A similar occurrence with tickets in this issue, as (15a). They had an oval 'O' in "Scottish" and "Postbus".

Known values:

25p	cerise	50p	pale lilac

17 Approximately three years had passed before further adjustments to the print of the next issue. The title had become smaller although the imprint remained in the same style as the previous issue.

Only one value known:

25p   rose pink

18 Later in 1985 another ticket was introduced - the title now in larger type with a bolder value. The imprint was the same as the previous issue.

Known value:-

50p   pale lilac

19 The third ticket for 1985 was different from other tickets. It was 1p brown with the title in the lower case with the imprint as previous.

20 In the late 1980's - possibly 1987/1988 a new print came forth. The title now showed a slight change - this being "Scottish Postbus Service", not "Services", as previously. Presumably this was a printers error. The imprint was said to be in small type. The values in this type are not known.

21 Also in the 1988/1989 period, a further change took place. The title reverted to "Services" and the value had become smaller and in thinner print. The imprint was now condensed.

Known values:-

10p   cream   50p   blue

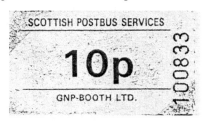

22 Further tickets followed at about the same time. The only difference was the value - now in thicker type.

Values known :-

10p   cream   £1.00   pale green

23 It is believed that before the end of 1988, roll tickets Printed by Automaticket: made an appearance. They were untitled.

Values known:-

20p   orange   50p   blue

24 When the first roll tickets appeared in 1974, this did not signal the end of the Almex 'A' or the Setright Speed machine. Setright Speeds continued to be purchased and put to work on certain services. They were not adapted to print a title, nor were printed rolls ever used.

Further Almex 'A' machines were also being obtained. At first, they were placed in service untitled. From early 1989 some machines were converted to print 'Royal Mail Letters Postbus Service'. Three different styles of printing plate are known.

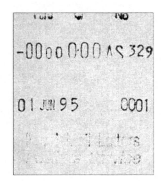

25 During 1990 new roll tickets made their appearance. These were titled "SCOTTISH POSTBUS SERVICE" in thin type, with a small value in the centre These had a miniature pence 'p' with G.N.P.-BOOTH LTD. imprint. This was the first issue with half moon corners.

Known values:-

3p	blue	50p	pink
5p	turquoise	50p	blue
10p	buff	£1.00	pale green
20p	orange	Concession	white

26 The issue that followed in 1991 was in similar style but has a larger pence 'p', and was printed on thick paper.

Known values:-

5p	pale green	50p	light blue
10p	primrose	£1.00	light brown
25p	pink	Concession	white
50p	cerise		

27 Roll tickets continued to appear with half-moon corners. This issue was in use during 1992 with title reverting to "SCOTTISH POSTBUS SERVICES", and reset into two lines, with bold value in centre. Printed on polished paper without printers imprint, but most probably by GNP-Booth Ltd.

Four values are known:-

5p	white	20p	orange
10p	primrose	£1.00	blue

28 The next issue that followed in 1992 was similar to the previous issue except that the value was much bolder and there was still no imprint.

Only one value is known:-

5p   red

29 The date of the following issue is not certain, but presumably dates from during 1993. The title was reset into a single line, in small. type, and reverted to "SERVICE" The values were elongated with large pence 'p'.

Two values are known:-

10p	pale yellow	50p	red

30 A change of style occurred in the following issue. The value became small and bold. Still without imprint. The title was now in elongated thin print.

Two values are known:-

20p	orange	25p	plum

31 A new Concession ticket appeared during 1995, the first for a few years. Title in large thin type without imprint; colour: white.

As stated earlier, the first Concessionary tickets to be accepted on a Scottish Postbus was issued between 1973 and 1975 on the Isle of Islay for use by their senior citizens. These were actually issued by the Post Office. Presumably, this facility was taken over from Highland Omnibuses Ltd.

Later, County Councils and Local Councils began to issue their own Concessionary tickets for the blind, the disabled, and senior citizens. These were gradually accepted on the Postbuses.

When the new County Councils and Unitary Authorities came into being in 1996, they brought forth new tickets and fare structures. A list of current Councils with Concessionary schemes is set out alongside.

Explorer, Freedom and Saver Tickets etc:
This type of ticket is not usually accepted on Postbuses but there may be exceptions to this.

Young Scot Cards and European equivalents:
One third off normal fare, (rounded to nearest 5p).

Regional/Islands Concessionary Card Holders:

Borders Council	Half adult fare
Clackmannan Council Stirling Council Falkirk Council }	Quarter adult fare
Dumfries & Galloway Council	£10 card - free. £2 card - 10p.
Fife Council.	Free.
Aberdeenshire Council. Moray Council. }	Half adult fare
Highland Council.	Half adult fare
Orkney/Shetland isles.	Half adult fare
West Lothian Council.	40p or 30p for one fare stage
Mid Lothian Council. East Lothian. }	35p flat fare
Argyle & Bute Council North Ayrshire Council. South Lanarkshire Council. }	35p flat fare
Perth & Kinross Council.	Quarter adult fare
Angus Council.	Senior citizens: quarter adult fare Disabled persons: 10p
Western Isles Council.	Half adult fare.

All fares are rounded up to the nearest 5p.

Blind persons producing the Scottish blind persons travelcard travel free.

Almex 'A' machines

Date of issue/return	Office issued to/returned to	Route no.	Machine Number
	Port Ellen	186	0108
	Cullipool	195	6010
	Lochmaddy	239/240	6256
	Killin	027	6321
	Elgol	106	6323
	Dunoon	193	6346
	Kinlochewe	091	6392
	Lairg	123	6399
	Larkhall	198	6548
	Dunoon	spare	6561
	Port Ellen	spare	6575
	Lairg	134	6582
	Inverness (spare)		6625
	Melvich	095	6628
	Timsgarry	242	6635
	Biggar	spare	6638
	Castle Douglas	044	6663
replaced	Inverness (spare)		6663
	Biggar		6683
2 Dec.1999	Inverness (spare)		6688
	Port Ellen	196	6692
	Inverness (spare)		6694
	Inverness (spare)		6715
	Lockerbie	051	6722
	Lochboisdale	234	7112
	Crianlarich	025	7184
	Pitlochry	spare	7185
	Biggar		7373
	Biggar		7387
	Nairn	124	7396
	Linlithgow	154 - 156	7407
	Aberfoyle	022	7441
	Castle Douglas	043	7469
	Dalkeith	152	7518
	Castlebay	233	7605
	Castle Douglas	045	7618
	Lochmaddy	239/241	7682
	Skerray	132	7685
	Dunbar	151	7689
	Inverness (spare)		7701
	Haddington	157	7718
	Lairg	105	7735
	Lairg	104	7749
	Lairg	spare	7841
	Lochmaddy	238	7872
	Inverness (spare)		7891
2 Dec.1999	Inverness (spare)		7895
	Port Ellen	185	7895
	Pitlochry	223	8005
	Aberfoyle	021	8008
	Shieldaig	131	8014
	Hawick	003	8037
	Callander	024	8083
	Applecross	092	8100
	Inverness (spare)		8108

Setright "Speed" Registers

Known machines and locations:

Machine No.	Location	Date
Z20	Cupar	1973
Z20	Galashiels	1978
Z21	Islay	1976
Z21	Thurso	1982
Z22	Nairn	1973
Z23	Crianlarich	1982
Z24	Castlebay	1973
Z24	Islay	1976
Z27	Laide	1976
Z32	Kylesku	1973
Z35	Lochmaddy	1973
Z37	Lockerbie	1973
Z37	Biggar	1976
Z37	Luing	1979
Z38	Elgol	1973
Z39	Lochmaddy	1973
Z39	Islay	1976
Z40	Skerray	1973
Z41	Craignure	1973
Z41	Islay	1976
Z42	Lochmaddy	1973
Z43	Galashiels	1973
Z51	Crianlarich	1979
Z51	Skerray	1981

	No.	Route	Commenced
Borders			
	009	Melrose - Galashiels - Lilliesheaf	28 Aug 1972
	003	Hawick - Bonchester Bridge - Southdeanrig	15 Oct 1974
	008	Kelso - Nenthorn - Hume - Stichell - Kelso	15 Oct 1974
	006	Kelso - Roxburgh	25 Mar 1975
	004	Hawick - Craik	15 Nov 1976
	007	Kelso - Smailholm	6 Dec 1976
	001	Duns - Abbey St.Bathans	18 Aug 1977
	005	Kelso - Hassington	5 Jun 1978
	002	Duns - Longformacus	13 Apr 1982
	014	Duns - Cranshaws	9 May 1994
Central			
	022	Aberfoyle - Kinlochard	8 Jan 1975
	027	Killin - Ardeonaig - Callander	24 Nov 1975
	023	Balfron - Fintry - Gribloch	9 Feb 1976
	024	Callander - Trossachs - Aberfoyle	30 Mar 1976
	021	Aberfoyle - Inversnaid	30 Mar 1976
	025	Crianlarich - Killin - Callander - Tyndrum	23 May 1977
Dumfries & Galloway			
	051	Lockerbie - St Anns	21 Apr 1973
	053	Thornhill - Moniave	28 Sep 1973
	044	Castle Douglas - Corsock	29 Aug 1974
	045	Castle Douglas - Mossdale	29 Aug 1974
	043	Castle Douglas - Auchencairn	6 Jun 1975
	042	Cummertrees - Powfoot - Annan - Newbie	17 Nov 1975
	052	Lockerbie - Waterbeck	17 Nov 1975
	049	Lockerbie - Corrie - Millriggs	19 Jan 1976
	041	Annan - Creca	19 Jan 1976
	047	Kirkcudbright - Gatehouse of Fleet	25 Oct 1976
	048	Kirkcudbright - Borgue - Lennox Plunton	25 Oct 1976
	050	Lockerbie - Hightae	12 Apr 1978
Fife			
	066	Cupar - Peat Inn	4 Dec 1972
	067	Leven - New Gilston	25 Mar 1975
Grampian			
	075	Forres - Braemoray	19 Jan 1976
	071	Aboyne - Logie Coldstone	26 Jan 1976
	078	Huntly - Lumsden	2 May 1977
	074	Banchory - Lumphanan	2 Aug 1982
	076	Huntly - Cabrach	8 Oct 1984
	077	Huntly - Clatt	7 Jan 1985
	072	Ballater - Glenshee - Linn of Dee	23 Apr 1990
Highland			
	106	Isle of Skye - Broadford	17 Apr 1972
	124	Nairn - Glenferness	28 Feb 1973
	130	Scourie - Kylestrome - Tarbet	1 Jun 1973
	122	Lochinver - Drumbeg	2 Jul 1973
	093	Ardgay - Easter Fearn - Strathoykel	21 Jul 1973
	098	Bettyhill - Kinbrace	10 Aug 1973
	094	Ardgay - The Craigs	20 Jun 1974
	128	Rogart - Sciberscross	30 Sep 1974
	109	Grantown-on-Spey - Lochindorb	4 Mar 1975
	100	Dingwall - Heights of Docherty	25 Mar 1975
	101	Drumnadrochit - Grotaig - Achtermarack	26 May 1975
	099	Dalwhinnie - Drumochter - Drummin	5 Nov 1975
	112	Invergarry - Kinlochbourn	2 Feb 1976
	125	Newtonmore - Kinlochlaggan	8 Mar 1976
	110	Halkirk - Glutt - Altnabreac	19 Jul 1976
	113	Invergordon - Kildermorie	18 Oct 1976
	096	Arnisdale - Kyle of Lochalsh	17 Apr 1978
	102	Isle of Skye - Portree- Dunvegan - Glendale	27 Nov 1978
	103	Isle of Skye - Dunvegan - Waternish	27 Nov 1978
	134	Tongue - Talmine - Tongue - Lairg	19 Nov 1979
	135	Thurso - Wick / Wick Airport	22 Nov 1982

No.	Route	Commenced
097	Fort William - Glen Etive - Fort William	5 Sep 1984
119	Kyle of Lochalsh - Plockton - Stromeferry	1 Jan 1985
132	Skerray - Tongue - Melvich	27 Oct 1986
115	Inverness - Moy - Tomatin - Coignafearn	27 Oct 1986
114	Inverness - Gorthleck - Killin	8 Jun 1987
127	Rogart - Muie and West Langwell - Lairg	18 Nov 1987
133	Strathconon - Beauly	22 Feb 1988
108	Gairloch - Melvaig - Redpoint	19 Sep 1988
118	Kyle of Lochalsh - Letterfearn	19 Dec 1988
116	John O'Groats - Wick	30 Jan 1989
095	Armadale - Melvich - Thurso	13 Feb 1989
111	Invergarry - Fort Augustus	19 Jun 1989
104	Durness - Lairg via Kinlochbervie and Scourie	10 Aug 1992
107	Fort William - Garvan (Circular)	2 Nov 1992
123	Drumbeg - Lochinver - Lairg	5 Apr 1993
091	Diabaig - Achnasheen	30 May 1994
092	Applecross - Toscaig - Torridon	27 Mar 1995
131	Shieldaig - Strathcarron - Torridon	27 Mar 1995
129	Scourie - Elphin - Lochinver	5 Feb 1996
105	Lairg - Durness - Lairg via Altnaharra	5 Feb 1996

Lothian

No.	Route	Commenced
151	Dunbar - Innerwick	4 Jun 1968
153	Haddington - Garvald	20 Jun 1974
155	Livingston - West Calder - Tarbrax	22 Aug 1974
154	Linlithgow - Blackness	08 Jan 1979
156	Linlithgow - Whitecross - Maddiston	23 Jan 1995
152	Dalkeith - Moorfoot - Temple	20 Nov 1995
157	Haddington - Humble	2 Nov 1998

Strathclyde

No.	Route	Commenced
184	Biggar - Tweedsmuir	11 Aug 1973
185	Port Askaig - Bowmore - Port Ellen - Ardbeg	1 Oct 1973
196	Isle of Islay: Portnahaven - Port Ellen - Ardbeg	1 Oct 1973
199	Tarbert - Skipness	17 Nov 1975
197	Isle of Tiree - Scarinish	27 Nov 1975
191	Isle of Colonsay - Oronsay	16 Feb 1976
195	Isle of Luing	3 May 1976
183	Biggar - Carnwath	16 Aug 1976
194	Inveraray - Dalmally	7 May 1977
188	Isle of Arran: Brodick - Pirnsmill - Whitefarland	31 Aug 1977
182	Biggar - Lanark	19 Sep 1977
192	Dalmally - Bridge of Orchy	20 Mar 1978
198	Strathaven - Dungavel	24 Apr 1978
193	Dunoon - Colintraive - Tignabruaich	3 Jul 1978
181	Biggar - Abington - Crawfordjohn	3 Jun 1987
202	Isle of Lismore Circular	13 Jun 1994
189	Isle of Arran Circular (North)	21 Nov 1994
190	Isle of Arran Circular (South)	21 Nov 1994
187	Isle of Mull: Salen - Ulva Ferry/Burg	21 Aug 1995
200	Inveraray - Lochgilhead	28 Dec 1995

Tayside

No.	Route	Commenced
211	Aberfeldy - Glenlyon - Lubreoch	3 Jan 1974
220	Kirriemuir - Glenclova	2 Sep 1974
221	Kirriemuir - Glen Prosen	2 Sep 1974
218	Dunblane - Braco - Langside	21 Sep 1976
222	Pitlochry - Dalnaspidal	22 Nov 1976
219	Kinross - Rumbling Bridge	7 Feb 1977
216	Blairgowrie - Glenshee	1 Apr 1978
214	Birnam - Aberfeldy	10 Feb 1979
223	Pitlochry - Rannoch Station	4 Jan 1989
215	Blairgowrie - Glenisla	5 Jun 1989
212/213	Aberfeldy - Killin - Aberfeldy	8 Jul 1992

Orkney & Shetland

No.	Route	Commenced
171	Isle of Bressay	6 Dec 1976
161	Isle of Rousay	23 Mar 1978

No.	Route	Commenced
Western Isles		
238	North Uist: Lochmaddy - Balivanich	16 Jun 1972
233	Isle of Barra: Castlebay - Eoligarry	17 Aug 1972
239	North Uist: Bayhead - Lochmaddy - Clachan	05 Apr 1996
240	North Uist: Lochmaddy - Sidinish - Baleshare	05 Apr 1996
242	Isle of Lewis: Timsgarry - Callanish - Stornoway	06 Apr 1996
234	North Uist: Lochboisdale - Balivanich Airport	13 Oct 1997

Notes: All routes as at January 2000.
Commencing dates are those for the routings as listed; some routes started at
earlier dates but with different routings.
Route numbers are those used in Postbus timetables; they are not shown on the buses.

The driver of the South Uist Postbus chats to a customer
[Photograph, courtesy Ken Ross]

Other Publications from
The Transport Ticket Society

London Transport Numerical Stage Punch Tickets - Bob Williamson
Checklists of all known "deaf and dumb" type punch tickets from 1933 onwards.

Part 1 - Tram and Trolleybus	**£3.50**
Part 2 - Central Buses	**£3.50**
Part 3 - Country Buses and Green Line Coaches	**£2.50**
Part 4 - Prepaids	**£3.50**
Part 5 - Miscellaneous	**£3.50**

London in 1997 - Brian Pask
Comprehensive survey of tickets and ticket systems in the Capital, covering bus, tube, rail and river services. **£2.50**

INTIS - Brian Boddy
The British Rail Intermediate Ticket Issuing System: a comprehensive guide in two volumes. (*) **£8.00**

Greater Manchester in 1998/9 - Paul J Smith and Brian Hughes
Complete survey of tickets and ticket systems, covering bus, tram and rail. (*) **£4.50**

The Tickets of the Grimsby & Immingham Electric Railway - Brian Pask
All known tickets described, with numerous illustrations, faretables and map. (*) **£4.75**

The Tickets of Hants & Dorset Motor Services 1920-1987 - Andrew Waller
Part 1 - Punch Tickets
Exhaustive history detailing all known punch tickets. Fully-illustrated with tickets, faretables and two maps. (*) **£5.50**

Part 2 - Machine, Emergency and Office Issued Tickets
Detailing machine tickets, seasons, emergencies and parcels tickets. Fully-illustrated with tickets and map. (*) **£5.50**

South Yorkshire Supertram - Fares and Ticketing - 1994-1997 - Dave Aspinwall
A compilation of tables and diagrams, detailing fares, tickets and machine validations. Fully illustrated. (*) **£5.50**

Tickets of the West Midlands PTE Part 4 - 1983-1986 - Robin Oliver
Details of all known tickets issued in the final years of the PTE as a bus operator. Fully illustrated. **£5.00**

"Omnibus Tickets" in London - J C Purton, Edited by Brian Pask
The "Omnibus Ticket"-titled issues used in London from horse-bus days onwards. Fully illustrated. **£3.50**

Tickets of the Liverpool Overhead Railway Company - Trefor David
An overview of the ticket system and tickets of this well-known line which closed in 1956. Fully illustrated. **£5.00**

* including illustrations in colour

All prices include postage and packing. Order from the Publication Sales Officer:

Steve Skeavington [X]
6 Breckbank,
Forest Town,
Mansfield,
NG19 0PZ

Why not join The Transport Ticket Society?

For membership details, send two first-class stamps to:

The Transport Ticket Society [X]
4 Gladridge Close
Earley, Reading
RG6 7DL

E-mail: courtney@gladridgecl.demon.co.uk

or visit our website: www.btinternet.com/~transport.ticket

Welsh and Scottish Postbus Tickets 1967-1999
Eric C. Moles

£3.50

ISBN 0 903209 53 5

ISBN 0-903209-53-5

9 780903 209533 >

IMPRINTED ON THE TICKET

Steve Skeavington

HENRY PRINTED IT !

N⁰. 382

CAR PARK
LONSDALE HOTEL

Date........................

5/- **5/- COACH**

Time ....

Registered No. ....

CONDITIONS OF ISSUE

Available on day of issue only.
Not Transferable. Ticket to be retained and
produced on demand.
Vehicles are admitted on the express condition
that the Proprietors of the Lonsdale Hotel
shall not be liable for loss of, or damage to
any vehicle or anything in, on or about any
vehicle, or for injury to any person using the
Park, however such loss, damage or injury
may be caused.

**The
Transport
Ticket Society**